This memory journal is lovingly
sponsored by

Clay County
SENIOR SERVICES

Introduction

I hope you enjoy the experience of writing your life's adventures in this book. This is your opportunity to share what's truly important with those you love. I know they will treasure this written legacy. They will appreciate your memories, dreams, and wishes. They will cherish your words and gain strength and knowledge from your joys and trials. They will have a new perspective on history—from your point of view (better than any history book). *You* have an interesting story to tell. No fame or fortune is required. Your words will be a lasting, meaningful, and priceless gift to present and future generations.

Since you are about to begin telling life stories, I'll share one of my own. I grew up in Erie, Pennsylvania, a very cold and blustery place with its close proximity to Lake Erie. Erie residents shovel about 140 inches of snow annually.

In 1978, my dad urged me to get a newspaper route. I decided that he had a good idea. I could use the money for school clothes and other necessities. Actually, I think dad just wanted to keep me busy and out of trouble. Little did I know that the paper route would become a part of my morning for the next *nine* years until I left for Otterbein College in 1987. Did I mention that Erie gets 140 inches of snow a year? It was tough delivering papers in two feet of snow. In the spring, it was hard to get out of bed at 5 a.m. and walk without fear through shadow-ridden, worm-covered streets. It took nerve to go door-to-door and ask customers to pay for their newspapers when I didn't think they had any money. It was maddening to do the same old thing almost every day for nine years.

What did I learn from this paper route? I learned that hard work does pay off (I earned a college scholarship from the newspaper). I learned that I _could_ make it if I just did not paralyze myself with fear (those awful shadows and worms). I learned that I was not alone (thanks goes to Mom, Dad, LeAnne, Ed, and Lance for all your help on many mornings). Finally, I learned that failure was not an option (the papers had to get delivered whether it was Christmas Sunday or any other day).

LifeBio has reminded me of my paper route since its humble beginnings in 2000 (or the idea stage in 1998). It has required constant hard work, long hours, courage, a very supportive family, teamwork, prayer, and commitment. We have had the privilege to create tools that will empower millions of people to create and share life stories. Your journal answers can even be transferred into www.LifeBio.com to create a finished, ready-to-print version of your life story, including digital photos, or even a beautiful hardcover book. Imagine the possibilities! *It's time to tell your story.*

Lisbeth "Beth" Sanders
Founder & President, LifeBio, Inc.

Acknowledgments

This book would not have been possible without the incredible support of so many.

I with to thank my husband and best friend, Jeff. He is a constant source of unfailing strength, good advice, and technical expertise. I would also like to thank my children, Melissa and David, for their patience and willingness to help me in any way they are able. In addition, it would have been impossible to finish this book without the help of my family and many of my closest friends. Late night phone conversations, ideas shared around the dinner table, and childcare help were critically important in making this dream come true.

Finally, I am reminded that "With God, all things are possible." It amazes me that this has finally come together, but I should not be amazed. It is an answer to prayer. I have asked, and I have received. Thanks again Lord. –Beth Sanders

It's time to tell your story™

Published by LifeBio, Inc.
The LifeBio Memory Journal
©2001, 2005, 2007, 2017, LifeBio, Inc.
Fourth Edition
Written by Lisbeth "Beth" Sanders
Technical Adviser: Jeff Sanders
ISBN 10: 0-9728751-2-3
ISBN 13: 978-0-9728751-2-7

Please direct any comments or questions regarding this book to LifeBio by using the contact information below:
LifeBio, Inc.
232 N. Main Street, Suite 2J
Marysville, Ohio 43040
866-LIFEBIO or 937-303-4576
Email: info@lifebio.com
www.lifebio.com

LifeBio and *It's time to tell your story* are registered trademarks of LifeBio, Inc., an Ohio corporation.

Table of Contents

This LifeBio is About...

_____
Full Name

_____
Maiden Name

_____
Street Address (Past or Present)

_____
City   State   Zip

_____
Phone

_____
E-mail

_____
Date of Birth

_____
Birthplace

Start Date _____   Completion Date _____

This book is dedicated to:

Section I:

The People Who Shaped You

Family History and Family Tree

a. What do you know about your ancestors? Did you or did your family emigrate from another country? How far back can you trace your family roots?

b. If your family history is recorded in a book or in another format, please reference this document here.

_____

_____

_____

_____

_____

_____

_____

_____

_____

_____

_____

_____

c. Share an interesting fact or a surprising piece of information from what you know of your family history.

_____

_____

_____

_____

_____

_____

_____

_____

_____

_____

_____

d. Describe your family tree including your parents (natural and/or adoptive), brothers, and sisters. Include grandparents, aunts, uncles, cousins, or others if you wish. (Remember you will have more opportunities in your LifeBio to talk about your family members. This is just a general overview.)

Mother

a. What is your mother's name (include maiden name), her date of birth, and her birthplace?

_____

_____

_____

_____

_____

_____

_____

_____

_____

_____

_____

b. Describe your mother's favorite memory of her childhood.

_____

_____

_____

_____

_____

_____

_____

_____

_____

_____

c. Share more details about your mother's childhood. How did your mother spend a summer day as a child? What was her favorite toy? Who was her best friend?

_____

_____

_____

_____

_____

_____

_____

_____

_____

_____

d. How would you describe your mother to someone who had never met her?

_____

_____

_____

_____

_____

_____

_____

_____

_____

_____

_____

_____

_____

e. Tell one of your most vivid and unforgettable memories
   of your mother.

_____

_____

_____

_____

_____

_____

_____

_____

_____

_____

_____

_____

f. What is a key lesson you learned from your mother?

_____

_____

_____

_____

_____

_____

_____

_____

_____

_____

g. What do/did you enjoy doing most with your mother?

_____
_____
_____
_____
_____
_____
_____
_____
_____
_____
_____
_____

h. What story does/did your mother always tell about you?

_____
_____
_____
_____
_____
_____
_____
_____
_____
_____
_____

i. What is/was one of your mother's favorite stories to tell?

_____

_____

_____

_____

_____

_____

_____

_____

_____

_____

_____

_____

j. Describe the work your mother does/did during her life.

_____

_____

_____

_____

_____

_____

_____

_____

_____

_____

_____

_____

k. What will you most remember about your mother?

_____

_____

_____

_____

_____

_____

_____

_____

_____

_____

_____

l. Did your mother pass any heirlooms, traditions, recipes, songs, or other important things on to future generations?

_____

_____

_____

_____

_____

_____

_____

_____

_____

_____

m. What are some skills, talents, or attitudes you feel you have inherited from
   your mother?

_____

_____

_____

_____

_____

_____

_____

_____

_____

_____

_____

_____

_____

_____

n. What is life like for your mother today? If she is deceased, how and when did
   she pass away?

_____

_____

_____

_____

_____

_____

_____

_____

_____

_____

_____

_____

Father

a. What is your father's name, date of birth, and birthplace?

_____

_____

_____

_____

_____

_____

_____

_____

_____

_____

_____

_____

b. Describe your father's favorite memory of his childhood.

_____

_____

_____

_____

_____

_____

_____

_____

_____

_____

_____

_____

c. Share more details about your father's childhood. How did your father spend a summer day as a child? What was his favorite toy? Who was his best friend?

_____

_____

_____

_____

_____

_____

_____

_____

_____

_____

_____

_____

_____

d. How would you describe your father to someone who had never met him?

_____

_____

_____

_____

_____

_____

_____

_____

_____

_____

_____

_____

e. Tell one of your most vivid and unforgettable memories of your father.

_____

_____

_____

_____

_____

_____

_____

_____

_____

_____

f. What is a key lesson you learned from your father?

_____

_____

_____

_____

_____

_____

_____

_____

_____

_____

_____

_____

g. What do/did you enjoy doing most with your father?

h. What story does/did your father always tell about you?

i. What is/was one of your father's favorite stories to tell?

j. Describe the work your father does/did during his life.

k. What will you most remember about your father?

l. Did your father pass any heirlooms, traditions, recipes, songs, or other
   important things on to future generations?

m. What are some skills, talents, or attitudes you feel that you've inherited from
   your father?

_____

_____

_____

_____

_____

_____

_____

_____

_____

_____

n. What is life like for your father today? If he is deceased, how and when did he
   pass away?

_____

_____

_____

_____

_____

_____

_____

_____

_____

_____

Maternal Grandparents (mother's parents)

a. What are your maternal grandparents' names, dates of birth, and birthplaces? Include your grandmother's maiden name if possible.

_____

_____

_____

_____

_____

_____

_____

_____

_____

_____

_____

_____

_____

b. Tell one of your most vivid and unforgettable memories of each maternal grandparent.

_____

_____

_____

_____

_____

_____

_____

_____

_____

_____

c. What is a key lesson you learned from your mother's parents?

_____

_____

_____

_____

_____

_____

_____

_____

_____

_____

_____

d. What do/did you enjoy doing most with your maternal grandparents?

_____

_____

_____

_____

_____

_____

_____

_____

_____

_____

_____

_____

_____

e. Can you recall stories told by your maternal grandparents?

_____

_____

_____

_____

_____

_____

_____

_____

_____

_____

_____

_____

_____

f. Describe the work your maternal grandparents do/did during their lives.

_____

_____

_____

_____

_____

_____

_____

_____

_____

_____

_____

_____

g. Did your maternal grandparents pass any heirlooms, traditions, recipes, songs, or other important things on to future generations?

_____

_____

_____

_____

_____

_____

_____

_____

_____

_____

_____

h. What are some skills, talents, or attitudes you feel you have inherited from your maternal grandparents?

_____

_____

_____

_____

_____

_____

_____

_____

_____

_____

i. What is life like for your maternal grandparents today? If they are deceased, how and when did they pass away?

_____

_____

_____

_____

_____

_____

_____

_____

_____

_____

Memorabilia

Maternal Grandparents (mother's parents)

Paternal Grandparents (father's parents)

a. What are your paternal grandparents' names, dates of birth, and birthplaces? Include your grandmother's maiden name if possible.

_____

_____

_____

_____

_____

_____

_____

_____

_____

_____

_____

b. Tell one of your most vivid and unforgettable memories of each paternal grandparent.

_____

_____

_____

_____

_____

_____

_____

_____

_____

_____

_____

c. What is a key lesson you learned from your father's parents?

_____

_____

_____

_____

_____

_____

_____

_____

_____

_____

_____

_____

d. What do/did you enjoy doing most with your paternal grandparents?

_____

_____

_____

_____

_____

_____

_____

_____

_____

_____

e. Can you recall stories told by your paternal grandparents?

f. Describe the work your paternal grandparents do/did during their lives.

g. Did your paternal grandparents pass any heirlooms, traditions, recipes, songs, or other important things on to future generations?

_____

_____

_____

_____

_____

_____

_____

_____

_____

_____

_____

_____

h. What are some skills, talents, or attitudes you feel you have inherited from your paternal grandparents?

_____

_____

_____

_____

_____

_____

_____

_____

_____

_____

_____

i. What is life like for your paternal grandparents today? If they are deceased, how
   and when did they pass away?

_____

_____

_____

_____

_____

_____

_____

_____

_____

_____

_____

Memorabilia

Brothers and Sisters

a. What are your siblings' names, dates of birth, and birthplaces?

_____

_____

_____

_____

_____

_____

_____

_____

_____

_____

_____

_____

_____

_____

b. How would you describe your brother(s) and/or sister(s) to someone who
   had never met him/her/them?

_____

_____

_____

_____

_____

_____

_____

_____

_____

_____

_____

_____

c. Tell one of your most vivid and unforgettable memories about each
   brother/sister.

_____

_____

_____

_____

_____

_____

_____

_____

_____

_____

_____

d. What is a key lesson you learned from your brother/sister?

_____

_____

_____

_____

_____

_____

_____

_____

_____

_____

_____

e. What was it really like growing up together? Was someone the teaser, the peacemaker, the food-thrower, or the one who always got angry first?

_____

_____

_____

_____

_____

_____

_____

_____

_____

_____

_____

_____

f. What did you enjoy doing most together when you were children?

_____

_____

_____

_____

_____

_____

_____

_____

_____

_____

_____

g. What do you enjoy doing together now?

_____

_____

_____

_____

_____

_____

_____

_____

_____

_____

_____

h. What story does your brother/sister tell about you?

_____

_____

_____

_____

_____

_____

_____

_____

_____

_____

_____

i. What will you most remember about him/her?

_____
_____
_____
_____
_____
_____
_____
_____
_____
_____
_____
_____
_____

j. What is life like for your brother/sister today? If deceased, how and when did he/she pass away?

_____
_____
_____
_____
_____
_____
_____
_____
_____
_____
_____

Other relatives or people that touched your life

a. What are the names, dates of birth, and birthplaces of the other relatives or people that are/were involved in your life?

_____

_____

_____

_____

_____

_____

_____

_____

_____

_____

_____

b. Tell one of your most vivid and unforgettable memories of each person.

_____

_____

_____

_____

_____

_____

_____

_____

_____

_____

_____

_____

c. What is a key lesson you learned from these relatives or loved ones?

d. What do/did you enjoy doing most with them?

e. Can you recall stories told by them?

_____
_____
_____
_____
_____
_____
_____
_____
_____
_____
_____
_____

f. Describe the work they do/did during their lives.

_____
_____
_____
_____
_____
_____
_____
_____
_____

g. Did they pass any heirlooms, traditions, recipes, songs, or other important
things on to future generations?

_____

_____

_____

_____

_____

_____

_____

_____

_____

_____

_____

_____

h. What are some skills, talents, or attitudes you feel you have inherited from
them?

_____

_____

_____

_____

_____

_____

_____

_____

_____

_____

_____

_____

i. What is life like for these relatives or loved ones today? If they are deceased, how and when did they pass away?

_____
_____
_____
_____
_____
_____
_____
_____
_____
_____
_____

Memorabilia

Section II:

Memories

Historical Events

Please put a check mark next to historical events below that are memorable to you or impacted your life in some way. After you have chosen the events, go to the following pages to explain why those events are memorable or how the events affected your life. These are just ideas. If you recall an event that is not on the list, please go ahead and write about it.

The News on the Day You Were Born

Transportation Before Automobiles

The Family Car

Railroad Trains

Telephone

Electricity in the Home

Air Travel

World War I

The Rise of Communism

Women's Right to Vote

Memorable Newspaper Headlines

Influence of Radio on Society

Influence of Movies on Society

Charles Lindbergh

Amelia Earhart

Prohibition

Stock Market Crash

The Great Depression

World War II

Pearl Harbor

The Holocaust

Atomic Bomb

The Rise of Suburbs

Influence of Television on Society

Korean War

Baby Boomer Generation

Civil Rights Movement

Nuclear War Threats

Assassination of John F. Kennedy

Assassination of Martin Luther King, Jr.

Rise of Rock 'n Roll

Vietnam War

Watergate

Women's Liberation Movement

Hostage Crisis in Iran

Rise of the Computer Age

Challenger Disaster

Persian Gulf War

Memorable Presidents and Other Leaders

Emergence of the Internet & Worldwide Web

Growth of the World Economy

Stock Market

Oklahoma City Bombing

Y2K - The Year 2000

Memorable Elections

September 11, 2001

Terrorism & Mass Shootings

Wars & Conflicts

Rise of Social Networks & Social Media

Smart Phones, Apple

The Olympics

Natural Disasters – Tsunamis, Earthquakes, Hurricanes, etc.

Concerns about the Environment

Mars and Space Exploration

Other Memorable Events...

Historical Event:

Historical Event:

Historical Event:

Historical Event:

Historical Event:

Historical Event:

Growing Up

a. What is your earliest memory?

_____

_____

_____

_____

_____

_____

_____

_____

_____

_____

_____

_____

_____

_____

b. Describe your childhood home, inside and outside.

_____

_____

_____

_____

_____

_____

_____

_____

_____

_____

c. Describe your town, neighborhood, and the environment around your childhood home. If you lived in the country, describe distant neighbors or favorite spots in the country. If you lived in the city or suburbs, take us down the street with you. Who were some of your most memorable neighbors? Describe the smells of your neighborhood (food cooking, smells from chimneys, or other memorable odors). Describe the types of businesses that existed there. What languages were spoken?

d. What made your neighborhood a place you loved, liked, or disliked?

e. Tell about your childhood friends and your favorite things to play. Describe a favorite hiding place or place to be alone.

f. What are some of your most vivid memories of being a child? Think about your bedroom, chores that were assigned to you, a new pair of shoes, a lemonade stand, the dinner table, or family pets. Think about all your senses. What did you see, hear, smell, taste, and feel?

_____

_____

_____

_____

_____

_____

_____

_____

_____

_____

g. How did your parents expect you to behave? Did you meet those expectations?

_____

_____

_____

_____

_____

_____

_____

_____

_____

_____

_____

h. If your parents were separated or divorced, describe your feelings about this.

_____

_____

_____

_____

_____

_____

_____

_____

_____

_____

i. What were your dreams and plans for the future? What did you want to be when you grew up?

_____

_____

_____

_____

_____

_____

_____

_____

_____

j. Why were you named what you were named? Were you named after someone?
   Did you ever have a nickname?

_____

_____

_____

_____

_____

_____

_____

_____

_____

_____

_____

_____

k. If you had money to spend as a child, what did you buy? Were you a better
   saver than spender?

_____

_____

_____

_____

_____

_____

_____

_____

_____

_____

_____

l. What was your favorite store? Describe it and tell how much it cost to buy
   common items or your special treats.

_____

_____

_____

_____

_____

_____

_____

_____

_____

_____

_____

m. Is there a special treasure or collection that you saved from your childhood?
   Tell about it.

_____

_____

_____

_____

_____

_____

_____

_____

_____

_____

_____

Childhood and Teen Favorites

a. What was your favorite doll or toy? Describe.

b. What was your favorite game? Describe.

c. What was your favorite dessert? Describe.

d. What was your favorite food? Describe.

e. What were your favorite clothes? Describe.

f. What was your favorite sport? Describe.

g. What was your favorite book? Describe.

_____
_____
_____
_____
_____
_____
_____
_____
_____
_____
_____
_____
_____
_____

h. What was your favorite movie? Describe.

_____
_____
_____
_____
_____
_____
_____
_____
_____
_____
_____
_____

i. What was your favorite radio and/or TV show? Describe.

j. Who was your favorite hero? Why?

k. Who was your favorite person to spend time with? Why?

_____
_____
_____
_____
_____
_____
_____
_____
_____
_____
_____

Memorabilia

Family Fun, Vacations, and Celebrations as a Child and Teenager

a. Describe your favorite celebrations when you were a child. Religious holidays? Christmas? Thanksgiving? Fourth of July? Reunions? Just "Get Togethers" for no special reason?

_____

_____

_____

_____

_____

_____

_____

_____

_____

_____

_____

b. Describe your family's reunions.

_____

_____

_____

_____

_____

_____

_____

_____

_____

_____

_____

c. Recall your favorite birthday party.

_____

_____

_____

_____

_____

_____

_____

_____

_____

_____

_____

_____

d. What would your family do for fun during the summer?

_____

_____

_____

_____

_____

_____

_____

_____

_____

_____

_____

_____

e. What would your family do for fun in the fall?

_____

_____

_____

_____

_____

_____

_____

_____

_____

_____

_____

f. What would your family do for fun in the winter?

_____

_____

_____

_____

_____

_____

_____

_____

_____

_____

g. What would your family do for fun in the spring?

h. What is/are your most memorable vacation(s) with your family as a child or teenager? Who did you see? What did you do? Where and when did you go? How did you travel?

Place of Worship and Faith as a Child and Teenager

a. Describe your church, synagogue, mosque, temple, or other place of worship when you were a child or teenager. Was its appearance traditional or modern? Was there a physical feature of this place that always struck you?

_____

_____

_____

_____

_____

_____

_____

_____

_____

_____

_____

_____

_____

_____

_____

b. What are your memories of your place of worship? Did you enjoy singing, reading scripture, spending time learning about your faith with other children, or other aspects? Recall your memories from this time.

_____

_____

_____

_____

_____

_____

_____

_____

_____

_____

_____

c. How did being a part of this place of worship affect your life and the life of your family when you were a child?

_____

_____

_____

_____

_____

_____

_____

_____

_____

_____

_____

_____

d. Describe your faith journey and your belief in God. What did you believe when you were a child and teenager? Did you understand your faith as a child or teenager? In other words, did the message really sink in?

_____

_____

_____

_____

_____

_____

_____

_____

_____

Elementary School Years

a. Describe your elementary school experience. How did you get to and from school? What did the school look like from the outside and inside? What was it like to walk in the halls, to play on the playground, to eat in the cafeteria, or to sit at your classroom desk?

_____

_____

_____

_____

_____

_____

_____

_____

_____

_____

_____

b. What was your favorite subject in school? What was your least favorite subject?

_____

_____

_____

_____

_____

_____

_____

_____

_____

_____

_____

_____

_____

c. What were your most memorable experiences from elementary school? (Think about school plays, scouting, projects, recess, awards, talent shows, etc.)

_____

_____

_____

_____

_____

_____

_____

_____

_____

_____

_____

d. Who was your favorite teacher? Least favorite? Why?

_____

_____

_____

_____

_____

_____

_____

_____

_____

_____

_____

e. What was the most important thing you learned in elementary school?

f. Who were your friends and what did you enjoy doing together?

g. How was your time spent when not in school? Describe any jobs you had or things you did for fun in the summertime at this age.

_____

_____

_____

_____

_____

_____

_____

_____

_____

_____

_____

Memorabilia

Junior High/Middle School Years

a. Describe your junior high or middle school experience. How did you get to and from school? What did the school look like from the outside and inside? What was it like to walk in the halls, to eat in the cafeteria, or to sit at your classroom desk?

_____
_____
_____
_____
_____
_____
_____
_____
_____
_____
_____
_____

b. What was your favorite subject in school? What was your least favorite subject?

_____
_____
_____
_____
_____
_____
_____
_____
_____
_____

c. What were your most memorable experiences from junior high/middle school? (Think about school dances, scouting, band, chorus, clubs, projects, school plays, talent shows, sports, etc.)

_____

_____

_____

_____

_____

_____

_____

_____

_____

_____

_____

d. Who was your favorite teacher? Least favorite? Why?

_____

_____

_____

_____

_____

_____

_____

_____

_____

_____

_____

_____

_____

_____

e. What was the most important thing you learned in junior high/middle
   school?

_____

_____

_____

_____

_____

_____

_____

_____

_____

_____

_____

f. Who were your friends and what did you enjoy doing together?

_____

_____

_____

_____

_____

_____

_____

_____

_____

_____

_____

_____

g. How was your time spent when not in junior high/middle school? Describe an after-school job or things you did for fun in the summertime at this age.

High School and Teenage Years

a. Describe your high school. How did you get to and from school? What did the school look like from the outside and inside? What was it like to walk in the halls, to eat in the cafeteria, or to sit at your classroom desk?

_____

_____

_____

_____

_____

_____

_____

_____

_____

_____

_____

_____

_____

_____

_____

b. What was your favorite subject in high school? What was your least favorite subject?

_____

_____

_____

_____

_____

_____

_____

_____

_____

_____

c. What were your most memorable experiences from high school? (Think about your first date, school dances, first time you drove a car to school, band, chorus, clubs, projects, school plays, talent shows, sports, or other moments.)

_____
_____
_____
_____
_____
_____
_____
_____
_____
_____
_____

d. Who was your favorite teacher? Least favorite? Why?

_____
_____
_____
_____
_____
_____
_____
_____
_____
_____
_____
_____

e. What was the most important thing you learned in high school?

f. Who were your friends and what did you enjoy doing together?

g. Remember a memorable or funny experience you had on a date.

_____

_____

_____

_____

_____

_____

_____

_____

_____

_____

_____

h. How was your time spent when not in high school? Describe an after-school job or things you did for fun in the summertime at this age.

_____

_____

_____

_____

_____

_____

_____

_____

_____

_____

_____

Military Service

a. In what branch of the service did you serve? Where and when did you serve?

b. Describe your basic training experience.

c. What became your area of expertise?

d. Describe your friendships during your service. Were people in your unit killed or taken prisoner? How did you feel?

e. Was there a time when you thought you were going to die? Describe this
   moment.

_____

_____

_____

_____

_____

_____

_____

_____

_____

_____

_____

_____

_____

_____

_____

_____

_____

_____

_____

_____

_____

_____

_____

_____

_____

_____

_____

_____

_____

_____

_____

_____

f. Share any combat or non-combat stories you wish to talk about. What was a day like for you? What is your most memorable moment from your military service?

_____

_____

_____

_____

_____

_____

_____

_____

_____

_____

g. How did your experience in the military affect your life and your family?

_____

_____

_____

_____

_____

_____

_____

_____

_____

_____

_____

Advanced Training and College

a. What college, university, or other type of advanced training program did you enroll in?

b. What did you choose to study and how did you pay for school?

c. If you went away to school, what was it like for both you and your parents when you left home?

_____

_____

_____

_____

_____

_____

_____

_____

_____

_____

_____

d. Are you glad you chose to study what you studied?

_____

_____

_____

_____

_____

_____

_____

_____

_____

_____

_____

e. Describe any memorable experiences from this time (fraternity/sorority times, jobs while in school, dorm life, your first roommate, friends you remember, your favorite/least favorite professor, etc.).

Memorabilia

Section III:

The Real World

Jobs and Careers

a. As you became a young adult, what lessons were you learning? Did you feel prepared for the "Real World"? Did it seem like a "jungle out there" or not?

b. Were you afraid that you would not find a job? Was it a good or a bad time to be coming out of school?

c. What was life like for you after finishing school?

_____

_____

_____

_____

_____

_____

_____

_____

_____

_____

_____

_____

_____

d. What was your first "real" job? What was a typical day like at your work?

_____

_____

_____

_____

_____

_____

_____

_____

_____

_____

_____

_____

_____

e. Describe your jobs or your career through the years and what you learned along the way.

_____

_____

_____

_____

_____

_____

_____

_____

_____

_____

_____

f. Have you ever been elected to public office? What was the process? How did it feel to become a public figure?

_____

_____

_____

_____

_____

_____

_____

_____

_____

_____

_____

g. What advice would you give to future generations about work?

_____

_____

_____

_____

_____

_____

_____

_____

_____

_____

_____

_____

h. What is your favorite work? What is your least favorite work?

_____

_____

_____

_____

_____

_____

_____

_____

_____

_____

_____

_____

i. Have you ever started your own business? Describe how this happened and the successes or challenges you encountered.

Family Fun, Vacations, and Celebrations as an Adult

a. Describe your favorite celebrations as an adult. Religious holidays? Christmas? Thanksgiving? Fourth of July? Reunions? Just "Get Togethers" for no special reason?

_____

_____

_____

_____

_____

_____

_____

_____

_____

_____

_____

_____

b. Describe your family's reunions.

_____

_____

_____

_____

_____

_____

_____

_____

_____

_____

_____

_____

_____

_____

c. Recall memorable birthday parties.

d. What does your family do for fun during the summer?

e. What does your family do for fun in the fall?

_____
_____
_____
_____
_____
_____
_____
_____
_____
_____
_____
_____
_____

f. What does your family do for fun in the winter?

_____
_____
_____
_____
_____
_____
_____
_____
_____
_____
_____
_____
_____

g. What does your family do for fun in the spring?

_____
_____
_____
_____
_____
_____
_____
_____
_____
_____
_____

h. What is your most memorable vacation? Who did you see? What did you do?
   Where and when did you go? How did you travel?

_____
_____
_____
_____
_____
_____
_____
_____
_____
_____
_____

Love

a. Have you found true love? Describe what true love means to you.

_____

_____

_____

_____

_____

_____

_____

_____

_____

_____

_____

_____

_____

_____

_____

_____

b. How did you meet that special person?

_____

_____

_____

_____

_____

_____

_____

_____

_____

_____

_____

_____

c. Do you believe in love at first sight?

_____
_____
_____
_____
_____
_____
_____
_____
_____
_____
_____
_____

d. What makes/made the person you love/loved so special?

_____
_____
_____
_____
_____
_____
_____
_____
_____
_____
_____
_____

e. What advice would you give to future generations about love?

Marriage

a. How did you meet your husband or wife?

_____

_____

_____

_____

_____

_____

_____

_____

_____

_____

_____

_____

_____

b. Where would you go on dates?

_____

_____

_____

_____

_____

_____

_____

_____

_____

_____

_____

_____

_____

c. What happened on the day you were engaged?

_____
_____
_____
_____
_____
_____
_____
_____
_____
_____
_____
_____
_____
_____
_____
_____
_____
_____
_____
_____
_____
_____
_____
_____
_____
_____
_____
_____
_____

d. Describe your wedding day including the actual date, what you wore, who your attendants were, what the weather was like, and where the wedding and reception were held.

e. Share memories from your honeymoon.

_____
_____
_____
_____
_____
_____
_____
_____
_____
_____
_____
_____
_____
_____

f. Describe your spouse to someone who has never met him or her. What makes him/her attractive?

_____
_____
_____
_____
_____
_____
_____
_____
_____
_____
_____

g. Describe your spouse's family and memories of times together.

_____

_____

_____

_____

_____

_____

_____

_____

_____

_____

_____

_____

h. What advice would you give to future generations about marriage?

_____

_____

_____

_____

_____

_____

_____

_____

_____

i. If you have experienced divorce or remarriage, you are welcome to share your memories and feelings.

Home as an Adult

a. Describe the places (cities, towns, homes, neighborhoods) where you have
   lived as an adult.

_____
_____
_____
_____
_____
_____
_____
_____
_____
_____
_____
_____
_____

b. What was your favorite place to live and what made that place special?

_____
_____
_____
_____
_____
_____
_____
_____
_____
_____
_____
_____
_____
_____

c. Describe your current home and what makes it uniquely yours.

Place of Worship and Faith as an Adult

a. Describe your church, synagogue, mosque, temple or other place of worship. Is its appearance traditional or modern? Is there a physical feature of this place that strikes you?

_____

_____

_____

_____

_____

_____

_____

_____

_____

_____

_____

b. What makes your place of worship special to you? How do you experience God?

_____

_____

_____

_____

_____

_____

_____

_____

_____

_____

_____

c. What touches you during the worship experience? Do you enjoy singing, praying, or other aspects of your time there?

_____

_____

_____

_____

_____

_____

_____

_____

_____

_____

_____

_____

_____

d. How has being a part of this place affected your life and the life of your family?

_____

_____

_____

_____

_____

_____

_____

_____

_____

_____

_____

_____

e. Describe your faith journey and your belief in God. What do you believe is the truth?

_____

_____

_____

_____

_____

_____

_____

_____

_____

_____

_____

_____

f. How have your beliefs changed over time? How have your beliefs remained the same through the years?

_____

_____

_____

_____

_____

_____

_____

_____

_____

_____

_____

Children and Parenthood

a. List the names and birthdates of your child or children. If your child/children is/are adopted, include an adoption date as well.

_____

_____

_____

_____

_____

_____

_____

_____

_____

_____

_____

_____

_____

b. Describe the day you held your child or each of your children for the first time and how you felt. Did you feel prepared, scared, happy, or worried?

_____

_____

_____

_____

_____

_____

_____

_____

_____

_____

_____

c. Tell a story about your child/children as a small child.

_____

_____

_____

_____

_____

_____

_____

_____

_____

_____

_____

_____

d. Tell a story about your child/children as a teenager.

_____

_____

_____

_____

_____

_____

_____

_____

_____

_____

_____

e. Tell a story about your child/children as an adult.

_____
_____
_____
_____
_____
_____
_____
_____
_____
_____
_____
_____

f. What traits of yours does your child/do your children have?

_____
_____
_____
_____
_____
_____
_____
_____
_____
_____
_____
_____

Children and Parenthood

g. What makes you proud to be his/her/their parent?

_____
_____
_____
_____
_____
_____
_____
_____
_____
_____
_____
_____
_____

h. What makes each child special?

_____
_____
_____
_____
_____
_____
_____
_____
_____
_____
_____
_____
_____

i. What is the best part of being a parent?

j. What is the hardest part of being a parent?

k. If you could go back and do it over, would you change anything?

l. What are some of the things you learned from your child/children?

m. Describe a time when you felt especially close to your child/children.

_____

_____

_____

_____

_____

_____

_____

_____

_____

_____

_____

_____

_____

n. What advice can you give about being a parent?

_____

_____

_____

_____

_____

_____

_____

_____

_____

_____

Grandchildren and Becoming a Grandparent

a. List the names and birthdates of your grandchildren.

_____

_____

_____

_____

_____

_____

_____

_____

_____

_____

_____

_____

b. Describe the day each of your grandchildren was born and how you felt on that day. Did you feel prepared, scared, happy, or worried?

_____

_____

_____

_____

_____

_____

_____

_____

_____

_____

_____

c. Recall stories of your grandchildren when they were very young.

_____
_____
_____
_____
_____
_____
_____
_____
_____
_____
_____
_____
_____

d. Recall stories of your grandchildren when they were teenagers.

_____
_____
_____
_____
_____
_____
_____
_____
_____
_____
_____
_____

e. Recall stories of your grandchildren when they were adults.

_____

_____

_____

_____

_____

_____

_____

_____

_____

_____

_____

_____

f. What traits of yours do your grandchildren have?

_____

_____

_____

_____

_____

_____

_____

_____

_____

_____

g. What makes you proud to be their grandparent?

h. What makes each grandchild special?

i. What is the best part of being a grandparent?

_____

_____

_____

_____

_____

_____

_____

_____

_____

_____

_____

j. What is the hardest part of being a grandparent?

_____

_____

_____

_____

_____

_____

_____

_____

k. If you could go back and do it over, would you change anything?

_____

_____

_____

_____

_____

_____

_____

_____

_____

_____

l. What are some of the things you learned from your grandchild/grandchildren?

_____

_____

_____

_____

_____

_____

_____

_____

_____

_____

m. Describe a time when you felt especially close to your grandchild/grandchildren.

_____

n. How do things change when you are a grandparent instead of a parent?

_____

o. What advice can you give about being a grandparent?

Everyday Moments

a. Do you have a special hobby such as woodworking, gardening, painting, or something else? Why do you enjoy doing this? Do you share this hobby with anyone close to you?

_____

_____

_____

_____

_____

_____

_____

_____

_____

_____

b. Do you have a collection? What do you collect and why is this something you enjoy?

_____

_____

_____

_____

_____

_____

_____

_____

_____

_____

_____

c. What do you think about current politics or other stories in the news?

_____

_____

_____

_____

_____

_____

_____

_____

_____

_____

_____

d. What is the best part of your day?

_____

_____

_____

_____

_____

_____

_____

_____

_____

_____

Everyday Moments

e. What do you like or dislike about your life right now?

f. Where is your favorite place to be in your home?

g. Where is your favorite place to visit, to take a walk, and to take a drive?

h. Who are your friends? Do you share coffee, talk on the phone, or visit each other regularly?

i. Do you have a best friend? If so, why are you such good friends?

Family Pets

a. What was your first pet and why did you pick this animal?

_____

_____

_____

_____

_____

_____

_____

_____

_____

_____

_____

_____

b. Did you always want a certain kind of pet but never got it?

_____

_____

_____

_____

_____

_____

_____

_____

_____

_____

c. Describe other family pets and how they became a part of your family.

_____

_____

_____

_____

_____

_____

_____

_____

_____

_____

_____

d. Tell about any pets you or your children had and include any memorable moments.

_____

_____

_____

_____

_____

_____

_____

_____

e. What did your pets teach you?

Friendship

a. Do you have a best friend? Why is he or she your best friend?

b. Share about a friendship that has meant a lot to you.

c. What makes your friend(s) so special?

d. What have you learned from friends?

e. Share about your friends and what you enjoy doing together.

_____
_____
_____
_____
_____
_____
_____
_____
_____
_____
_____

f. Have your friends helped you get through difficult times?

_____
_____
_____
_____
_____
_____
_____
_____
_____
_____
_____
_____

Volunteerism and Philanthropy

a. Are you or were you a volunteer for an organization? What have you done as a
   volunteer?

_____

_____

_____

_____

_____

_____

_____

_____

_____

_____

_____

_____

b. Why is volunteering important to you?

_____

_____

_____

_____

_____

_____

_____

_____

_____

_____

_____

_____

c. Why do you feel strongly about a particular cause?

_____

_____

_____

_____

_____

_____

_____

_____

_____

_____

_____

d. What could you say to encourage others to be involved in volunteerism?

_____

_____

_____

_____

_____

_____

_____

_____

_____

_____

_____

_____

e. Do you support a particular cause through philanthropy? If so, why do you think this is important?

_____

_____

_____

_____

_____

_____

_____

_____

_____

_____

_____

_____

_____

f. How do you see your support of this cause benefiting others now and in the future?

_____

_____

_____

_____

_____

_____

_____

_____

_____

_____

_____

_____

Memorabilia

Section IV:

Bringing It All Together

Family Stories and Heirlooms

a. What are your favorite family stories? Please share a few of them.

b. Describe any family heirlooms you have inherited.

c. What will you pass on to future generations (recipes, furniture, quilts, stories, other things) and what do these things tell about you and others from the past? Share some family recipes if you wish.

Beliefs

a. It's been said that "The best things in life are free." Is this true?

_____

_____

_____

_____

_____

_____

_____

_____

_____

_____

_____

_____

_____

_____

_____

b. What are your core beliefs? What is important to you? How do you want people to remember you?

_____

_____

_____

_____

_____

_____

_____

_____

_____

_____

_____

_____

c. Do you have a motto that you live by? This could be something you think of that gets you through good times and bad times.

_____

_____

_____

_____

_____

_____

_____

_____

_____

_____

_____

_____

d. Do you consider yourself patriotic?

_____

_____

_____

_____

_____

_____

_____

_____

_____

_____

_____

_____

_____

e. Do you believe in God? Describe your faith and its effect on your life. Include a prayer or other thoughts if you wish.

_____

_____

_____

_____

_____

_____

_____

_____

_____

_____

_____

f. When you die, what will happen?

_____

_____

_____

_____

_____

_____

_____

_____

_____

_____

_____

_____

g. When times are difficult, what do you do to get through these times?

Opinions and Tough Questions

a. What was the best time of your life? Why?

b. What was the worst time of your life? Why?

c. How was your life affected by the death of friends or family members? Are there memorable funerals you can recall?

_____
_____
_____
_____
_____
_____
_____
_____
_____
_____
_____
_____
_____

d. Were you ever considered a hero? What happened?

_____
_____
_____
_____
_____
_____
_____
_____
_____
_____
_____
_____
_____

e. Were you ever famous (at least 15 minutes of fame)?

_____
_____
_____
_____
_____
_____
_____
_____
_____
_____
_____

f. Did anyone ever save your life? Describe.

_____
_____
_____
_____
_____
_____
_____
_____
_____
_____
_____

g. Was there a time in your life when you thought you were about to die?

h. What is your most embarrassing moment? If you have more than one, go ahead and include them all!

i. If you are a sports fan, what do you think is the single greatest sports moment of all time? Why was this such a memorable event for you?

_____
_____
_____
_____
_____
_____
_____
_____
_____
_____
_____

j. Did you ever experience prejudice? What happened? How did it change your view of the world?

_____
_____
_____
_____
_____
_____
_____
_____
_____
_____
_____
_____

k. What is the greatest invention that has come along in your lifetime so far? Why was this invention important to you?

_____
_____
_____
_____
_____
_____
_____
_____
_____
_____
_____
_____

l. Who do you most resemble in your family? Who resembles you?

_____
_____
_____
_____
_____
_____
_____
_____
_____
_____
_____
_____

Life

a. What are your secrets for living the good life?

b. What does it take to succeed in life?

c. Is there something you have always wanted to do that you have never done?

_____
_____
_____
_____
_____
_____
_____
_____
_____
_____
_____
_____
_____
_____

d. What has life taught you?

_____
_____
_____
_____
_____
_____
_____
_____
_____
_____
_____
_____
_____
_____

Lessons Through the Years

a. What did you dream about when you were a child or teen?

_____

_____

_____

_____

_____

_____

_____

_____

_____

_____

_____

_____

b. What did you wish for in your 20's?

_____

_____

_____

_____

_____

_____

_____

_____

_____

_____

_____

_____

c. What did you learn about yourself in your 30's?

d. What did you achieve in your 40's?

e. What did you hope for in your 50's?

_____
_____
_____
_____
_____
_____
_____
_____
_____
_____
_____
_____
_____

f. What did you dream about in your 60's?

_____
_____
_____
_____
_____
_____
_____
_____
_____
_____
_____
_____
_____

g. What did you discover in your 70's?

h. What did you enjoy in your 80's?

i. What did you wish for in your 90's?

_____

_____

_____

_____

_____

_____

_____

_____

_____

_____

_____

_____

j. What did you like about life at age 100+?

_____

_____

_____

_____

_____

_____

_____

_____

_____

_____

_____

The Future

a. What do you think the future will be like? Any predictions?

_____

_____

_____

_____

_____

_____

_____

_____

_____

_____

_____

_____

_____

_____

b. What do you want to be sure that future generations never forget about your family's past background and beliefs?

_____

_____

_____

_____

_____

_____

_____

_____

_____

c. Imagine that future generations are reading this 20 years or perhaps 100 years from now. What would you like to say to them? What hopes do you have for them?

Notes

Notes

Notes

Notes

Notes

Notes

Notes

Notes

Notes

Notes

Notes

Notes